Climbing in the Dark

Dramatised from his own story
by Nick Warburton

Illustrated by Martin Cottam

Oxford University Press

Climbing
in the
Dark

Oxford University Press, Great Clarendon Street, Oxford OX2 6DP

Oxford New York
Athens Auckland Bangkok Bogota Buenos Aires Calcutta
Cape Town Chennai Dar es Salaam Delhi Florence Hong Kong
Istanbul Karachi Kuala Lumpur Madrid Melbourne Mexico City
Mumbai Nairobi Paris São Paulo Singapore Taipei Tokyo
Toronto Warsaw

and associated companies in
Berlin Ibadan

Oxford is a trade mark of Oxford University Press

© David Calcutt 1998

First published 1998

Adapted from the novel **Climbing in the Dark** by Nick
Warburton, published by Oxford University Press in 1996.

ISBN 0 19 918798 3

Designed by Holbrook Design Oxford Limited

Printed in Great Britain

Cast list

Tess – a young housemaid

Mrs Hutton – the housekeeper at
Dr Gooch's house

Dr Gooch – the master

Harriet – his daughter

Fry – a chimney sweep

Will – Fry's apprentice

Introduction

Climbing in the Dark has been written in the style of a stage play.

There are three ways of performing this play.

1 You can read it in a group. (If you do this, make sure you read the stage directions as well as the speeches.)

2 You can perform it very simply, using only chairs and tables and imagining the rest of the set. (If you do it this way, you can make the sound of knocking on doors by stamping a foot.)

3 You can also perform it as a full play with painted scenery. (For example, you can make the railings, the rocking horse, the door in the cellar, etc.) The stage directions describe everything you are likely to need to do this.

A note on the set

When planning what sort of set to use, remember that if you use more complicated scenery, you must allow more time to change it between scenes. *Climbing in the Dark* is quite a fast-moving play, so if you do decide to perform it with scenery, try to think of ways of making the scenery as simple as possible.

Scene 1

In the hall.

*The hall is a big, empty room.
It has no furniture but there is a
large door at the back.*

*We can hear someone knocking on
the door.* **Mrs Hutton**, *the
housekeeper, hurries in.*

Mrs Hutton   Now what? Now what? Never a moment's peace.

*She opens the door and sees Tess
holding a small case.*

Tess   Please, ma'am...

Mrs Hutton   Not today, thank you. We're far too busy.

Tess   Please, ma'am. I'm Tess.

Mrs Hutton   Tess? Tess?

Tess   Yes.

Mrs Hutton   Oh, *Tess*. The new housemaid. But you've come
to the wrong door, girl.

Tess   Oh dear. What shall I do?

Mrs Hutton	This is the hall. Only proper visitors come to this door. The servants come in by the door round the back.
Tess	I'm sorry, ma'am. I didn't know.
Mrs Hutton	And don't call me 'ma'am'. I'm a housekeeper, not a lady. You must call me Mrs Hutton.
Tess	Yes, ma'am... I mean, Mrs Hutton.
Mrs Hutton	Well, come in, come in.

Tess steps into the hall.

Mrs Hutton   You'll sleep in the attic, but first you must come down to the kitchen and have some milk. Then I can tell you all you need to know.

*As they are about to move off, **Dr Gooch** enters. He is looking rather severely at his watch.*

***Dr Gooch** sees Mrs Hutton and stops.*

Gooch   Ah, Mary.

Mrs Hutton   Good morning, Dr Gooch.

*She makes a curtsey, then nudges Tess. **Tess** makes a curtsey.*

Gooch   *(Seeing Tess)* And who is this?

Mrs Hutton   This is Tess, Dr Gooch. The new housemaid.

***Tess** makes another curtsey.*

Tess   How do you do, sir?

Gooch   Yes, yes. Very well, thank you, Tess. Now then, Mary. We're taking tea with the Athertons this afternoon. I want you to make sure that the coach will be ready on time.

Mrs Hutton   Yes, Dr Gooch.

                   She is about to hurry off when there is another knock at the door.

Mrs Hutton   Oh, my stars! More knocking. We're all in a rush today, Dr Gooch, and no mistake.

Gooch	See to the coach, Mary. See to the coach. Tess can answer the door.

> *Mrs Hutton* runs off. *Tess* opens the door and *Harriet* tumbles in.

Harriet	Oh, Mary, Mary, you've got to help. *(Looking at Tess)* You're not Mary. Where's Mary?
Gooch	Calm down, Harriet.
Tess	I'm Tess, miss. The new housemaid.
Harriet	Oh. Well, you've got to help me with Belle, Tess. She's been rolling in puddles. We'll have to scrub her down.
Gooch	No, Harriet. Not you. Young ladies don't do things like that.
Harriet	Oh, Papa!
Gooch	Where is Belle?
Harriet	I had to tie her to the railings. She was being such a pest.
Gooch	Then fetch her in. Tess can clean her up.
Harriet	*(Sighing)* Oh, Papa!

Gooch   And don't sigh like that, Harriet. Young ladies never make such ugly sounds. Up to the nursery with you. You must get yourself ready. We're going to see the Athertons, remember, so you must look your best. Hurry, hurry!

He hurries off.

Harriet   Oh, Tess! I'm never allowed to do anything in this house. I have to be so pretty and polite all the time. I hate it.

Tess	Yes, miss. Sorry, miss.
Harriet	And you'll have to look after Belle. You are lucky, Tess.
Tess	Yes, miss. Is she your sister, miss?
Harriet	What?
Tess	Is Belle your sister, miss?
Harriet	*(Laughing)* No, of course not! I haven't got a sister. Anyway, I wouldn't tie her to the railings, would I?
Tess	No, I suppose not, miss.
Harriet	No, Belle is our little dog. I say, Tess. Let's bring Belle in and we can both clean her up.
Tess	But, miss, your pa said...
Harriet	Oh, we won't tell Papa.

Mrs Hutton *hurries on.*

Mrs Hutton	Are you still here, Miss Harriet? Your papa says you must hurry up to the nursery now.
Harriet	Oh, Mary!
Mrs Hutton	Off with you, my girl. You don't want to make him cross, do you?

Harriet begins to leave.

Harriet	*(Leaving)* The nursery! I hate that too. Perhaps one day something interesting will happen in this house.
Mrs Hutton	Now then, Tess. Fetch that dog in and bring her down to the kitchen. There's lots to do before the coach is ready.

Tess runs off one way and Mrs Hutton runs off the other way.

Scene 2

In the kitchen.

Mrs Hutton and Tess are sitting at a large table. There are some pots and pans about and a door at the back.

Tess is drinking milk.

Mrs Hutton	Just look at you, Tess. You're splashed all over. That Belle!
Tess	She's a lively little thing, Mrs Hutton. She wouldn't stay still.
Mrs Hutton	Have you dried her?
Tess	Yes.
Mrs Hutton	And tied new ribbons in her hair?
Tess	Yes, Mrs Hutton. She got really cross and snappy about it.
Mrs Hutton	She does. She's always cross and snappy. Well, it's done and finished so I can tell you about your duties...

There is a knock at the door and they both jump.

Mrs Hutton	Oh no. Not him!
Tess	Who is it?

There is another knock.

Mrs Hutton	It's Mr Fry, the chimney sweep. And he can wait.

She takes a drink and ignores the next knock. Then she gets up slowly and opens the door. **Fry** *enters, looking cross and carrying some poles.*

Fry	What kept you?
Mrs Hutton	We're busy down here, Mr Fry.
Fry	Busy? Huh! *(Turning to call over his shoulder)* Don't stand there gawping, you little rat. Fetch in some of them poles.

Will, *Mr Fry's apprentice, comes in with some more poles. He is a small, crouching, frightened figure.*

| **Mrs Hutton** | You've got a new boy, I see, Mr Fry. |
| **Fry** | A boy, Mrs Hutton? A rat on two legs more like. And an expensive one, too. |

> ***Will** puts the poles down and starts to cough.*

| **Fry** | And you can cut that out, you maggot! |
| **Mrs Hutton** | Why, he's skinny as railings. |

Fry   Of course he's skinny. He's got to get up chimneys, hasn't he? If he was plump he'd get stuck.

Tess   I think he needs a little water.

Fry   He needs a clip round the ear.

Mrs Hutton   *(Firmly)* Water, Mr Fry. You take your things through and I'll see to the boy.

Fry	But...
Mrs Hutton	Go on, Mr Fry. I'll bring him to you in two shakes.

Mr Fry moves off, mumbling. Before he leaves, he turns.

Fry	Don't pamper the little brat, that's all.

*He goes out. **Will** coughs again and **Mrs Hutton** helps him to sit down at the table.*

Mrs Hutton	You ought to be home in bed, my chicken.
Will	I ain't got no bed. I got a bit of straw on the floor.
Mrs Hutton	What's your name, boy?
Will	Will.
Mrs Hutton	Will what?
Will	Just Will. I don't know no other name. My father sold me to Mr Fry, to go up chimbleys.
Tess	Sold you? Your own father?

Will	Yes. 'E took me to Fry's 'ouse one day and then went 'ome without me. I found meself in this cellar full of brushes and things. Then I knowed. I was sold, to go up chimbleys.
Tess	But that's terrible.
Will	That's fathers for you, miss. They're all the same.
Mrs Hutton	Whatever must it be like, climbing about in chimneys?
Will	It's 'orrible, miss. The bricks stay so 'ot it 'urts, and the chimbley's dark and it twists about so you don't know where you are. And Mr Fry, 'e puts vinegar on me elbows and knees and stands me before the fire till I'm nearly roasted up.
Tess	But why does he do that?
Will	To 'arden the skin, miss. So I can grip on the chimbleys.
Mrs Hutton	Well, Will, there's some milk, and there's a spoon, and there's a pot of honey. You help yourself to that.

*Will eats ravenously. **Mrs Hutton** moves away from the table. She is upset. **Tess** joins her.*

Mrs Hutton	Poor little chap. Just look at him.
Tess	Is Mr Fry really so cruel? It's just not fair.
Mrs Hutton	That it isn't, Tess. Not fair at all. Now, you go up to the attic and set your things out. I'll look after Will.

*Tess goes off one way and **Mrs Hutton** gently leads Will off the other.*

Scene 3

In the corridor.

There is no furniture in the corridor but perhaps there are a few pictures on the walls.

***Mr Fry** is pacing up and down. He is very angry.*

Fry   Where is he? Where's the maggot got to?
(Shouting) Will! Will! Come out here, you devil!

Tess comes running on.

Tess What is it, Mr Fry? What's wrong?

Fry He's gone! The skinny rat's gone!

Tess Will?

*Mrs Hutton comes running on
from the other direction.*

Mrs Hutton Whatever is all this racket?

Tess Will's missing.

Fry That ratbag of a boy's gone up the chimney but
he ain't come down.

Mrs Hutton Oh, my stars. The poor mite!

Fry Poor? I'll have his bones for broth when I get
hold of him.

Mrs Hutton *(Clapping her hands at Fry)* Don't you talk so
cruel, Mr Fry.

Fry And don't you clap at me, missus. I ain't a bird.

Mrs Hutton Then stop flapping. He hasn't done it on
purpose, has he?

Fry	Oh, hasn't he? If that's what you think...

He is interrupted by a loud scream off stage.

Mrs Hutton	Lawks!

Fry	What the blazes was that?

Mrs Hutton	It's Miss Harriet. Come along, Tess. We must see what's the matter.

Mrs Hutton and Tess begin to hurry off. Fry calls after them.

Fry	Oi! What about the missing rat?

Mrs Hutton	(*Turning round*) He's just taking a rest, poor thing. He'll turn up.

Fry	But...

Mrs Hutton	Don't make a fuss, Mr Fry. You know where he went, so why don't you stick your head up the chimney and look for him?

Fry looks furious. Mrs Hutton grabs Tess and takes her off.

Scene 4

In Harriet's room.

*The room has a window and a door. There is a large cupboard in one corner. Some toys are scattered about. To one side is a chair, with **Harriet** hiding behind it. **Will** is lying in a heap on the floor behind a rocking horse.*

***Mrs Hutton** and **Tess** enter and stand for a moment looking round.*

Mrs Hutton   No one here.

Harriet   Help me, Mary. Please.

Tess	She's behind the chair, Mrs Hutton.
Mrs Hutton	Miss Harriet?

Harriet dashes out and clings to
Mrs Hutton.

Harriet	Oh Mary!
Mrs Hutton	There, there. You're quite safe...
Harriet	No, Mary. There's a creature in here. A monster...
Mrs Hutton	Don't be silly. Of course there isn't.
Harriet	There is! Over there. Look!

She points at the rocking horse.
Mrs Hutton *and* ***Tess*** *look at*
each other. Then ***Tess*** *creeps over*
to take a closer look.

Harriet	Be careful! Be careful!
Tess	I think it's Will.
Mrs Hutton	*(Moving closer)* Oo-er, so it is.
Harriet	*(Catching hold of Mrs Hutton again)* Please get rid of it. It's left paw prints on the rugs and...

*She points at Will again. He
moves slightly and* **Harriet**
screams.

Harriet   It's moving!

Mrs Hutton   He won't harm you, miss. It's only Will.

Harriet   Will?

                   Slowly **Will** *begins to recover.*

Mrs Hutton   The chimney sweep's boy. He must've fallen
                 down the chimney and knocked himself out.

Harriet   I don't care what it is, Mary. Just get rid of it.

Tess   He's not an 'it'; he's a boy.

> As she speaks, **Will** sits up and
> rubs his head.

Will   Where am I? What's going on?

Mrs Hutton   You're in the nursery, boy. You've come down
the wrong chimney.

Harriet   How horrible! I'm going to call Papa!

*She tries to dash off but **Mrs**
Hutton catches her.*

Mrs Hutton   Now you just calm yourself, miss. The little lad's
hurt himself and we can't go giving him back to
old Fry just yet.

Harriet   But why not?

Mrs Hutton   Because he'll beat him, that's why not.

Harriet   Then I'm going to hide again.

***Harriet** runs as far away from
Will as possible. She covers her
eyes but peeps through her fingers
as **Mrs Hutton** goes to help Will
up. He groans and coughs.*

Mrs Hutton   Can't you see, Miss Harriet? He's had a fright.
(To Will) You're all right now, Will. That's it.
Take it easy.

***Harriet** has been watching this.
She has crept closer and stands
behind Mrs Hutton.*

Harriet   But what's the matter with him?

Mrs Hutton   He's been made to climb up chimneys, miss.

Tess	Where it's dark and the bricks are still hot.
Harriet	Oh, no!
Mrs Hutton	And he lives in a cellar with no bed.
Tess	And his father sold him to Mr Fry, and Mr Fry is cruel, miss.
Harriet	But that's terrible!
Mrs Hutton	So we can't hand him over just yet, can we?
Harriet	No, Mary. We certainly can't.

Gooch and *Fry* are heard talking
to each other off stage.

Tess	What was that?
Mrs Hutton	There's someone coming. Go and see, Tess.

Tess runs to look off stage.

Tess　　　　It's Mr Fry and Dr Gooch. They're in the corridor, trying all the doors.

Will　　　　Oh no, I'm done for now.

Harriet　　　No. We must hide the boy. And we must clear up this mess. Put him in the toy cupboard, Mary. And Tess, help me to tidy up!

Tess　　　　Yes, miss. Right away, miss.

　　　　　　　Tess and Harriet collect up the toys and try to brush away the dirt where Will fell. Mrs Hutton bundles Will into the cupboard. The activity comes to a stop. They stand and listen.

Gooch　　　*(Off stage)* But he must be somewhere! This is ridiculous!

Mrs Hutton　Your papa's awfully angry, Miss Harriet. Perhaps we ought to let him know Will's here, and make up some excuses for the lad.

Harriet　　　No. We shan't hand him over at all. We'll set him free!

Tess Set him free?

Mrs Hutton But, Miss Harriet...

Fry and *Gooch* burst in.

Fry	He must be here. We've looked every other blooming place.
Gooch	Please, sir. Control your language in front of my daughter.
Harriet	Hello, Papa. What's going on?
Fry	Beg pardon for barging in, missie, but have you seen a rat-faced scrawny bean-pole pass through?
Harriet	A what?
Gooch	Mr Fry's boy has gone missing. Has he been in here?
Harriet	Of course not, Papa.

Fry wanders around, looking from side to side.

Fry	That's odd, then. The boy's missing, and there's screams in this room...
Gooch	Mr Fry, if my daughter says she has not seen him, you may take her word for it. I suggest we go downstairs and look there.
Fry	But ...

Gooch   *(Firmly)* Downstairs, Mr Fry.

> *Fry scowls and begins to move off. Gooch follows. The others sigh with relief. Then Will coughs. The two men stop.*

Fry   What was that?

Mrs Hutton   *(Pretending to cough)* Oh dear, master. I do beg your pardon. A bit of a cough...

> *But Will coughs again and Fry goes to the cupboard and opens it. Will tumbles out. Fry grabs him.*

Fry   Got you, you scheming bag of bones!

Gooch	Harriet!
Tess	Please, Dr Gooch. Don't blame Miss Harriet. She only...
Gooch	Be quiet! *(To Harriet)* You must have known he was here, Harriet.
Will	She didn't, mister. I 'id meself and she didn't know nothing about it...
Gooch	*(Shouting)* And you be quiet, too! Take him out, Fry. Harriet, I shall speak to you about this later.

> *Fry takes **Will** out. **Gooch** follows.*

Harriet	Oh dear.
Mrs Hutton	We've made it worse for the lad now. And Dr Gooch knows I was part of it. He could turn me out for this.
Harriet	He can't!
Mrs Hutton	You know he can, Miss Harriet, and you know what it'll mean if he does. It'll be the end of me.

> ***Mrs Hutton** begins to cry.*

Harriet   If you are turned out, Mary, I shall run away.

Tess   Oh, no, miss!

Harriet   But we must find that boy first. I won't have him beaten.

Tess   But how can we find him? Mr Fry will take him away and that will be that.

Harriet   If only we knew where Fry lives.

Harriet walks up and down, thinking.

Tess   I'm so sorry, Mrs Hutton.

Mrs Hutton   It's not your fault, Tess, but if I'm turned out...

Tess   He won't do that, will he?

Mrs Hutton   He might. Of course he might. Dr Gooch hates it when people don't tell the truth. Oh, Tess, he'll never trust me again. Oh, the shame, the shame of it.

                  Tess puts an arm round Mrs Hutton. Harriet has stopped to look out of the window.

Harriet   Tess! Mary! Come and look at this!

Tess joins her at the window. ***Mrs
Hutton****, still crying, follows.*

Tess   What is it, miss?

Harriet   Look down there, in the street.

Tess   Where?

Harriet   Don't you see? That cart. It's Fry's.

Tess   Oh, yes. And Will is with him.

Harriet   And it's got Fry's name painted on the side. His
                    name and address. So now we know where he
                    lives!

Tess   Where?

Harriet   A place called Cobble Yard. Do you know where
                    that is, Mary?

Mrs Hutton   *(Still sniffing)* Yes, miss. It's down by the river,
                    near the big bridge.

Harriet   Then you can go there, Mary.

Mrs Hutton   *(Shocked)* What?

Harriet	You can go there and find poor Will.
Mrs Hutton	Me? But, Miss Harriet, I'm already in trouble with your papa...
Harriet	But we have to find Will, don't we?
Mrs Hutton	*(Sighing)* Yes, miss. Of course, miss.
Tess	No. Let me go.
Harriet	You?
Tess	I know Cobble Yard, Miss Harriet. Will you let me go? Please, miss. I can be ever so quick and nimble.
Mrs Hutton	No, Tess. This is your first day and...
Tess	I know the place, Mrs Hutton. And I'm young and I can nip about so no one knows I'm there.
Harriet	That's right, Tess. You must go. *(Taking Tess by the hands)* Thank you, thank you. Now, we must plan this carefully. We have to be quick.

Harriet walks up and down again, thinking.

Mrs Hutton	*(Quietly, to Tess)* You'll get in trouble, too, Tess. I can't let you go.
Tess	It's better if I do, Mrs Hutton. You've got more to lose.
Mrs Hutton	But you'll be disgraced, Tess, and you might not get another job...
Tess	We haven't got time to think about that now.

>   *Harriet stops walking and clicks
>   her fingers.*

Harriet	I know! I'm going to the Athertons with Papa, and our carriage goes right by the river, so we can take you.
Mrs Hutton	No, no, Miss Harriet. That'll never do. How can poor Tess go with you in the carriage? Your papa will never allow it.
Harriet	Not *in* the carriage, Mary. At the back. Under the flap where we put the cases.
Mrs Hutton	What?

Harriet	Tess can hide. Papa won't even know she's there. *(To Tess)* Just find out where Will is and tell us what you see. That will be enough to start with.
Tess	Yes, miss.
Harriet	Now, Mary, you tell Tess how to get into the back of the carriage and then take her down to the street. I must get myself ready.

Harriet *hurries out.*

Mrs Hutton	Are you sure about this, Tess?
Tess	Of course. I want to help Will, too.
Mrs Hutton	Then I'll take you out the back way when the carriage turns up. It'll have a canvas sheet on the back. You can nip under that when no one's looking.
Tess	A canvas sheet. Yes. All right.
Mrs Hutton	*(Squeezing Tess by the hand)* You are a brave girl, Tess. Thank you. If you lose your job, I'll speak up for you. I'll do my best to keep you from going hungry.

Tess   Thank you.

Mrs Hutton   Now, we must hurry. Good luck!

They hurry off.

Scene 5

We are in a street. There are some railings with Fry's sign hanging on them and a gap between them where it looks as if some steps lead down to his cellar.

***Harriet** runs on, pulling **Tess** behind her.*

Harriet   This is the place. I'm sure it is.

Tess   Yes, look; there's the sign.

Harriet   Good. Are you all right, Tess? It was rather rocky in the carriage.

Tess   Yes, miss. Thank you, miss. I was bumped about but I'm all right.

Harriet   It must've been so stuffy in there, and dark.

Tess   It was. I couldn't see a thing, miss, and I didn't know where to jump out.

Harriet   I know. That's why I'm here. But I can't stop long. Papa will wonder where I am.

Tess   But how did you manage it, miss? Isn't he looking for you?

Harriet	No. I dropped my handkerchief out of the window so we had to stop. Wasn't that clever? Fry will be down those steps, in that cellar. Do you think we should take a look?
Tess	I will, miss. You haven't got time...
Harriet	I wonder if Will's down there, too. Oh, I wish I could go with you, Tess.
Gooch	*(Off stage)* Harriet? Where are you?
Tess	You'd better go now, miss. I think your pa's coming to look for you.
Harriet	Oh no! I must dash.

She runs and then turns back to Tess.

Harriet	Oh, I do wish I could stay and help!
Tess	Quickly, Miss Harriet! Go!
Harriet	I'm going, I'm going. Do what you can, Tess. And good luck to you!
Gooch	*(Off stage)* Harriet! Harriet, where are you? What is going on, child?

Harriet   Coming, Papa!

She runs off and **Tess** *is left alone.*
She turns and walks towards the
gap in the railings.

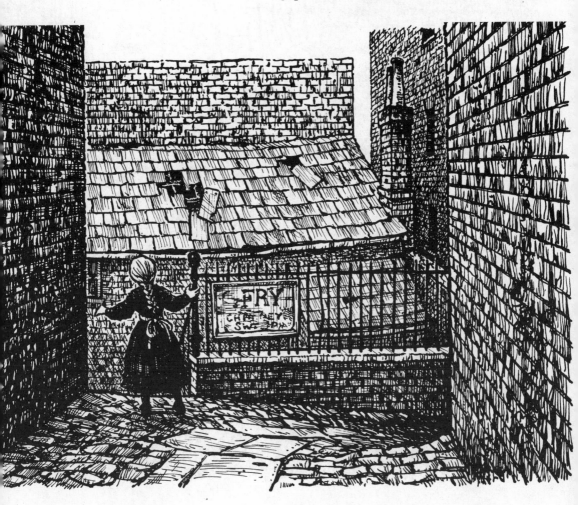

49

Scene 6

In the cellar, a dark brick room.
Fry *is asleep in a big chair. Near him is a large bunch of keys. At the back is a door with bars.* ***Will*** *is curled up on the floor behind this door.*

Tess *comes on and sees Fry in his chair. She tiptoes past him to whisper through Will's door.*

Tess   Will. Will, are you awake?

Will   *(Waking)* No. Don't 'it me again, master.

Fry moves about in his sleep but doesn't wake up.

Tess   Ssh! Will, it's me. Tess.

Will   *(Appearing at the bars)* Ooh, miss. What are you doing 'ere?

Tess   I've come to help you. Fry's asleep. You could come out with me now.

Will   No, miss. 'E'd beat me rotten...

Tess   He won't catch you, Will. If we're quick we can get away and he'll never know.

Will	But I can't, miss. The door's locked and 'e's got the keys.
Tess	Of course. I saw them on the arm of his chair. If I could just get hold of them...
Will	No, 'e'll wake up and there'll be bad trouble for you and all.
Tess	But I've got to try something. Wait there.
Will	I ain't got no choice, miss. I got to wait 'ere.
Tess	Yes, of course.

She creeps over to Fry's chair and very carefully tries to pick up the keys. She gets hold of them but **Fry** *moves in his sleep and puts his hand over them. Gently, gently she pulls them out of his fingers and goes back to Will.*

Will	Well done, miss. I thought 'e was waking up just then.
Tess	He will wake up soon. We've got to be quick.

*She unlocks the door and **Will** crawls out. They move slowly past Fry. At the last moment **Fry** stretches and puts his legs out and **Tess** falls over them.*

Fry   *(Waking up)* What? What's going on?

Will   Run, miss! Run!

                   ***Fry** jumps up and makes a grab at Tess. She squirms out of the way.*

Fry   Thief! I'm being robbed!

Tess	Help! Help!
Will	This way! Over here!

> *Fry turns and sees Will behind him. He moves slowly towards Will with his arms outstretched. **Will** backs away.*

Fry	Why, it's you, you ratbag!
Tess	Get out, Will! Get out!
Will	I can't leave you here with 'im. 'E's a monster.
Fry	Oh, I'm a monster, am I? Well, I'll show you what monsters do to skinny rats who try to sneak off.
Tess	Leave him alone!
Fry	And you keep quiet, you little thief. I'll deal with you later.

> *He lunges at Will. **Will** ducks and runs behind him. **Fry** turns round and lunges again. Again he misses and tumbles through the barred door. **Tess** shuts the door and locks it.*

Will	Oh, well done, miss! You've locked 'im in 'is own cellar!
Fry	Let me out of here! I'll have your bones for broth, the pair of you!
Tess	Then I certainly shan't let you out, you disgusting man. Come on, Will!

Will and Tess run, leaving Fry to shake the bars and shout.

Fry	Let me out of here! Let me out!

Scene 7

Back in the street, outside the cellar.

Will and Tess are standing by the railings. They are breathing hard, as if they have been running.

Will   We've done it, miss. We're free!

Fry   *(Shouting off stage)* Let me out of here, you thieving maggots!

Tess   We've got to keep going, Will. Run.

They run again, but Gooch and Harriet have come on. Will and Tess run straight into them. Gooch grabs Will.

Gooch   What is the meaning of this? What do you think you're doing?

Harriet   Oh, Tess! You've got him!

Will   It's all right, mister. I've bin rescued.

Gooch   Rescued? This is disgraceful. *(To Tess)* You have no right to do this...

Harriet   But I told you, Papa, that man is cruel...

Gooch   I know what you told me, Harriet. That's why
we came back. This stupid girl has caused no
end of trouble and I shall have to put it right.

58

Tess	Please, sir, I... I...
Gooch	Where is Mr Fry now?
Fry	*(Shouting off stage)* Aargh! You wait till I get hold of you!
Gooch	What is that noise?
Tess	I think it's Mr Fry, sir.
Fry	*(Shouting off stage)* Help! Let me out of here, for pity's sake!
Harriet	*(Happily)* Oh yes. That's Fry all right.
Gooch	Harriet! *(To Tess)* What on earth is the matter with the man?
Tess	He's a bit cross, sir. I've locked him in.
Harriet	Oh, well done, Tess!
Gooch	Be quiet, Harriet! She has not done well; she has done very badly.
Tess	But, sir, I only meant to...

Gooch	It doesn't matter what you meant. We must release Mr Fry immediately.
Will	No! Please...
Gooch	Of course he must be released. Show me where he is.

Tess leads them to the gap in the railings.

Scene 8

Inside the cellar.

*Tess, **Dr Gooch**, **Will** and **Harriet** approach the barred door.*

Gooch   Fry? Is that you?

Fry   *(Looking through the bars)* Dr Gooch? Get me out of here! There's been a terrible crime.

Gooch   All right, don't make such a fuss, man. *(To Tess)* Now, unlock the door. *(She hesitates)* Unlock the door!

*She unlocks the door and **Fry** bursts out. He immediately grabs **Will**.*

Fry   Now you'll pay, you snivelling wretch!

Will   Keep 'im off me! Keep 'im off!

Gooch   Stand still, man! There's no need to be so rough.

Fry   He has to learn what's right and wrong.

Gooch   And so he shall. But leave him alone until I can sort this business out.

Fry	*(Politely)* Of course, sir. Whatever you say, sir.
Gooch	Thank you. *(To Tess)* I can see now. You are to blame for everything.
Harriet	No, Papa!
Gooch	You have led my daughter astray. I should, perhaps, call the police ...

Tess	Please, sir, no.
Fry	That's right, sir. Get her taken away.
Gooch	I should, Tess, because you have tried to steal Fry's apprentice away from him. The police will tell you that.
Harriet	You can't, Papa! She's done nothing wrong.
Gooch	And I keep telling you she has. You can see that Mr Fry is a decent man.

Fry gives a sickening smile.

Fry	That's right. I'm just a law-abiding citizen, sir.
Gooch	*(To Tess)* I will let you off this time, girl, but I cannot have you in my house. Do you understand me? You must collect your things and leave this evening. *(To Will)* And you, boy, get back to your master straight away.
Will	Please! Don't make me go back!
Fry	Yes, come to me, my lad. Don't be afraid. We'll forgive and forget, shall we?
Gooch	There. You see, you'll come to no harm.

Harriet	But, Papa, he's just pretending to be nice.
Will	No!
Gooch	Now, boy. You know you must.

Will tries to run off but Gooch catches him by his shirt. The shirt is pulled aside to show red marks on Will's back. Everyone is still for a moment.

Gooch	How did you get these marks?
Will	'E beat me, sir, for being so bad. Please, don't make me go back.
Fry	Why, you lying vermin!
Gooch	Silence! *(To Tess)* Did you know he was beaten like this?
Tess	Yes, sir.
Harriet	We've been trying to tell you, Papa.
Gooch	In that case, Fry, I think you have some questions to answer.
Fry	It's lies, sir, all lies...
Gooch	These marks aren't lies. They're real enough. How did he get them? *(No answer)* How did he get them?
Fry	*(Suddenly shouting)* Because I beat him! But he was a wilful rat. He asked for it! And he's my rightful property, so hand him back to me!

Gooch	If you think so, Mr Fry, perhaps you'd like to call a policeman and make a complaint.
Fry	There ain't no need for that now...
Gooch	Then kindly stay where you are and close your mouth. *(To Will)* Don't you worry, my boy. I promise that you'll never be beaten like that again.

Scene 9

In the kitchen.

Mrs Hutton *is cooking,* **Tess** *is peeling apples and* **Harriet** *is sitting at the table listening.*

Mrs Hutton	Oh, I wish I'd been there to see Fry's face.
Harriet	It went all red. He was so angry, Mary.
Mrs Hutton	Terrible. That man should be sent away to the other side of the world.
Tess	They can't do that, Mrs Hutton. It's not a crime for a man to beat his apprentice.

Mrs Hutton	Well, it should be.
Harriet	Yes, it should be. Perhaps one day it will be.
Tess	Anyway, Fry won't beat them any more. Thanks to Dr Gooch.

Mrs Hutton	I told you he was a good man, Tess. He might look stern but he's got a heart of gold.
Harriet	And he'll keep an eye on old Fry, to make sure he's still behaving himself.
Mrs Hutton	Oh, he'll behave himself now all right. There'll be no more beatings for Fry's boys.
Harriet	That reminds me. I wonder how our new boot boy is getting on.

> *Will hurries in. He is clean and tidy and he carries a pair of shiny boots.*

Will	Look at these, Mrs 'Utton. You can see your face in 'em.
Mrs Hutton	Well done, Will. The master will be pleased.
Will	I 'ope so, Mrs 'Utton. I want to please 'im.
Mrs Hutton	And so you shall. You keep working away like that and he'll be very pleased. We'll all be pleased, Will.
Will	Oh, yes, Mrs 'Utton. All of us. Very pleased indeed.

Will smiles broadly and rubs
harder at the boots.

THE END

Treetops Playscripts
Titles in the series include:

Stage 10
The Masked Cleaning Ladies of Om
by John Coldwell;
adapted by David Calcutt
   single: 0 19 918780 0
   pack of 6: 0 19 918781 9

Stupid Trousers
by Susan Gates;
adapted by David Calcutt
   single: 0 19 918782 7
   pack of 6: 0 19 918783 5

Stage 11
Bertha's Secret Battle
by John Coldwell;
adapted by David Calcutt
   single: 0 19 918786 X
   pack of 6: 0 19 918787 8

Bertie Wiggins' Amazing Ears
by David Cox and Erica James;
adapted by David Calcutt
   single: 0 19 918784 3
   pack of 6: 0 19 918785 1

Stage 12
The Lie Detector
by Susan Gates;
adapted by David Calcutt
   single: 0 19 918788 6
   pack of 6: 0 19 918789 4

Blue Shoes
by Angela Bull;
adapted by David Calcutt
   single: 0 19 918790 8
   pack of 6: 0 19 918791 6

Stage 13
The Personality Potion
by Alan MacDonald;
adapted by David Calcutt
   single: 0 19 918792 4
   pack of 6: 0 19 918793 2

Spooky!
by Michaela Morgan;
adapted by David Calcutt
   single: 0 19 918794 0
   pack of 6: 0 19 918795 9

Stage 14
Petey
by Paul Shipton;
adapted by David Calcutt
   single: 0 19 918796 7
   pack of 6: 0 19 918797 5

Climbing in the Dark
adapted from his own novel
by Nick Warburton
   single: 0 19 918798 3
   pack of 6: 0 19 918799 1